50 SIMPLE
L.E.D. CIRCUITS

GW00360654

by
R. N. SOAR

BERNARD BABANI (publishing) LTD
THE GRAMPIANS
SHEPHERDS BUSH ROAD
LONDON W6 7NF
ENGLAND

PLEASE NOTE

Although every care has been taken with the production of this book to ensure that any projects, designs, modifications and/or programs etc. contained herein, operate in a correct and safe manner and also that any components specified are normally available in Great Britain, the Publishers do not accept responsibility in any way for the failure, including fault in design, of any project, design, modification or program to work correctly or to cause damage to any other equipment that it may be connected to or used in conjunction with, or in respect of any other damage or injury that may be so caused, nor do the Publishers accept responsibility in any way for the failure to obtain specified components.

Notice is also given that if equipment that is still under warranty is modified in any way or used or connected with home-built equipment then that warranty may be void.

© 1981 BERNARD BABANI (publishing) LTD

First Published — June 1981
Reprinted — June 1989

British Library Cataloguing in Publication Data
Soar, R. N.
  50 simple L.E.D. circuits — Book 2
  1. Light emitting diodes — Amateurs' manual
  I. Title
  621.3815'3043   TK9965
  ISBN 0 85934 062 7

Printed and Bound in Great Britain by Cox & Wyman Ltd, Reading.

CONTENTS

Circuit No.   **Page**

1	LED Test Circuit	1
2	Diode Tester	2
3	Improved Diode Tester	5
4	"Heads or Tails" Circuit	5
5	Unijunction LED Flasher	5
6	Portable Television Battery Monitor	8
7	Car Voltage Probe	9
8	Logic Level "1" Detector	10
9	Improved Logic Probe	10
10	Opto Isolator	12
11	Low Voltage Stabiliser	13
12	Numbers Toy	14
13	SCR Tester	15
14	NPN Transistor Tester	17
15	1½ Volt Cell Tester	18
16	Numeral "1" Display	19
17	Matching LEDs for Brilliance	21
18	Using LEDs on AC	22
19	The "2-LED" LED	23
20	"Magic Boxes"	23
21	3-Colour LED	25
22	2/3 Colour LED	26
23	Super "Magic Boxes"	28
24	AND Gate	28
25	NAND Gate	29
26	OR Gate	30
27	Exclusive OR Gate	31
28	NOR Gate	32
29	Rectifier Tester	33
30	Simple Rectifier Test	34
31	Simple Changeover Circuit	35
32	2-Colour Changeover Circuit	36
33	ZN414 IC Supply	37
34	Simple "Snap" Indicator	37
35	Stable 1mA Current Source	40

Circuit No.		Page
36	Simple 3 Digit Display	40
37	Current Flow Indicator.	42
38	Improved "6" Display for CA 7-Segment Display	44
39	Simple Ni-Cad Recharger	44
40	555 LED Flasher.	45
41	Flashing Seconds Display	45
42	Simple Signalling Device.	48
43	Precision Voltage Reference	48
44	Fuse Tester	48
45	Simple Timer	51
46	Flourescent Indicator Device Filament Tester.	52
47	Magnet Operated LED	54
48	Variable Capacitor Tester	54
49	LM3909 Flasher	56
50	LED "Line of Light"	57

INTRODUCTION

This book is the result of further experiments and tests carried out after the publication of my book No. BP42 "50 Simple LED Circuits" by Bernard Babani (publishing) Ltd. in 1977. As a result certain ideas have had to be modified.

It was stated in my first book that the longer lead of the LED is the cathode, this was the case with every LED tested. However, since the publication of that book, LEDs appeared which have the longer lead connected to the *Anode,* this is against the usual convention that the cathode of a diode is identified, but it seems that at least one major manufacturer produces LEDs with a longer anode lead.

This means that LEDs must always be checked for polarity before being soldered into circuit (see Circuit 1).

Red LEDs seem to be much more robust than green or yellow ones. Several of the original green LEDs used failed after several months for no apparent reason. LEDs can be destroyed by excessive current or a relatively low reverse voltage but the green LEDs failed in circuits where neither cause was possible. The reason for this sudden failure remains unknown. The lifetime of a LED is predicted as many years with a very gradual reduction in light output over the period. No red LED has failed in this way. LEDs can be used on low voltage A C but there is a possibility that the LED could be destroyed by the reverse voltage, a silicon rectifier should be connected to protect the LED, as described later.

Many of the circuits are shown as powered by 3 volt or 9 volt batteries, batteries are expensive, but at least this means that the circuits are perfectly safe for anyone to experiment with. However, one or two circuits are clearly marked as being not suitable for beginners.

ABBREVIATIONS USED

A	Anode
A C	Alternating Current
C A	Common Anode
C C	Common Cathode
D C	Direct Current
D P D T	Double Pole Double Throw Switch
	(Two circuit changeover switch)
G	Gate
K	Cathode
LED	Light Emitting Diode
S C R	Silicon Controlled Rectifier
	(Thyristor)
S P S T	Single Pole Single Throw Switch
	(ON/OFF)

This is a simple circuit to determine the polarity of a LED.

The longer lead of the LED should always be connected as shown. At switch position 1, if the LED glows the longer lead is the ANODE. At switch position 2, if the LED glows the longer lead is the CATHODE. See Circuit 1.

If the LED does not glow in position 1 or 2 it is faulty but check carefully that the two LED leads are not touching and causing a short circuit.

If you are testing a large number of surplus or "bargain price" LED's you may get weird results. One Green LED was found which glowed brightly in one direction (anode positive) but also glowed dimly but distinctly in *reverse*. You might come across a LED which glows equally brightly in either

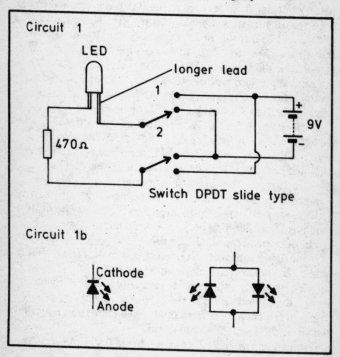

direction, this is a "twin" LED as shown in Circuit 1b, i.e. two LEDs connected in Inverse Parallel, or a LED which glows Red in one direction and Green in the other (see later Circuits).

The resistor value shown is 470Ω this makes the tester suitable for any colour LED, if Red LEDs only are tested the value can be $1k\Omega$ or $2.2k\Omega$ this will still give quite a bright glow but will reduce the current drawn from the battery.

The switch is a miniature D P D T slide type details of the several ways in which the D P D T slide switch can be used are given later.

CIRCUIT 2
Diode Tester

Power rectifiers can be tested easily with a LED and a 3 volt battery but signal diodes such as the 0A91 are intended to pass only a small current and might be damaged. This circuit uses a low current to test the diode, the test current is amplified by a transistor and the transistor turns the LED on. The test current through the diode is about 1mA. The transistor is a 2N697, this is a general purpose type available at low cost and is used in several other circuits in the book. Any transistor which is described as "similar to the 2N697" is perfectly suitable.

If the diode under test is connected as shown the LED will glow if the diode is functional. The diode should also be tested in the reverse direction and if the diode is functional the LED will not glow. A diode which is functional conducts in one direction, forward bias — anode positive, and does *not* conduct in the reverse direction, reverse bias — anode negative. If the diode conducts in both directions it is short circuit, if it conducts in neither direction it is open circuit. A short circuit or open circuit diode is useless.

If the diode appears to be open circuit make certain that it is actually connected into the circuit properly.

The cathode of a signal diode is usually indicated by a ring next to the cathode lead.

If you remove diodes from old broken radios you may find that the cathode end is coloured red.

Germanium signal diodes are numbered 0A91, 0A90,

2

0A81 etc. diodes of American or Japanese origin have type numbers 1N60 etc. For further details on signal diodes and their uses see Book No. BP36 50 Circuits using Germanium, Silicon and Zener Diodes, published by Bernard Babani (publishing) Ltd. Tr1 the 2N697 is functioning as a current amplifier.

Germanium diodes are not perfect rectifiers they do pass a small current in the reverse direction, this reverse current when amplified may be sufficient to cause the LED to glow very dimly, this does not mean that the diode is faulty it is quite normal.

Sometimes the anode and cathode of a diode are indicated as A and K.

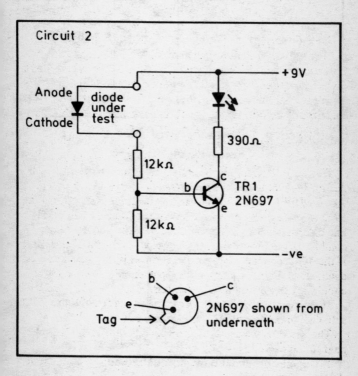

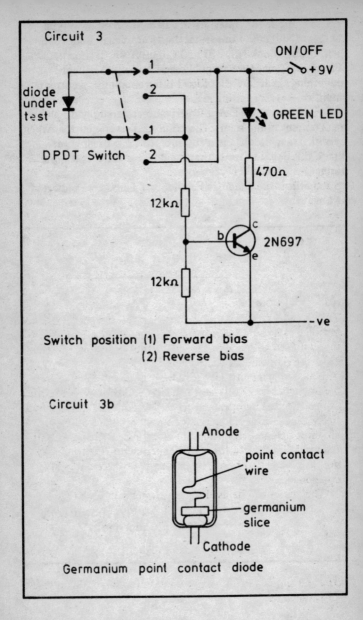

Circuit 3

ON/OFF

+9V

diode under test

DPDT Switch

GREEN LED

470Ω

12kΩ

12kΩ

2N697

b c e

−ve

Switch position (1) Forward bias
(2) Reverse bias

Circuit 3b

Anode

point contact wire

germanium slice

Cathode

Germanium point contact diode

4

CIRCUIT 3
Improved Diode Tester

Circuit 3 is developed from circuit 2.

In this circuit a Green LED is used as an indicator, a higher value of current limiting resistor is used. The effect is that the faint glow given by a Red LED, when the diode under test is reverse biased, is absent. The LED will still glow if the diode under test is faulty.

A D P D T slide switch reverses the connections to the diode under test, position (1) is forward bias, (2) is reverse bias. A S P S T is fitted as ON/OFF switch, see Circuit 3. Circuit 3b shows the construction of a typical point contact germanium diode. The point contact wire may sometimes be referred to as a "whisker".

CIRCUIT 4
"Heads or Tails" Circuit

This is a circuit based on the multivibrator, the circuit oscillates between two states on or off as indicated by the 2 LED's. When the switch S1 is operated the circuit "sticks" in one position either LED1 or LED2 will be glowing.

Note the symmetry of the circuit. It is not possible to predict which LED will light when S1 is operated. The circuit can be checked by operating S1 a 100 times and noting how many times LED1 is illuminated it will be about 50, if the circuit is operated 500 times it will be about 250 i.e. in half the total number. In the actual experiments, the total may not be exactly 50 or 250, this being due to tolerances in components.

The circuit can be used for experiments in probability.

CIRCUIT 5
Unijunction LED Flasher

This is a simple circuit using a unijunction transistor to turn a LED on and off.

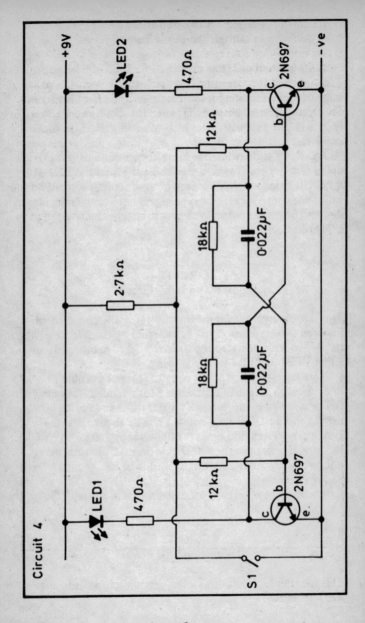

Circuit 4

R1 and C1 determine the flashing rate. The TIS43 uni-junction is shown but the "bargain price equivalent" UT46 is also suitable in the circuit.

A normal transistor has two junctions but the unijunction only has one hence its name. A transistor has connections emitter, base and collector but the unijunction has connections emitter base one and base two (e, b1, b2). A lower value for C1, e.g. 47 μF 16V will increase the flashing rate. Unlike an incandescent light the LED can flash at very high speed if the value of C1 is reduced further the LED will flash so fast that the eye cannot resolve the individual flashes and the LED will appear to be glowing continuously.

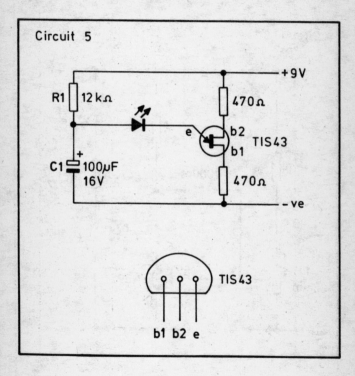

CIRCUIT 6
Portable Television Battery Monitor

This circuit is designed for use with a portable television operated from a storage battery. The circuit senses the voltage and when this drops below a preset level the LED glows. This can indicate that the battery needs recharging. The drain on a car battery by a portable black and white set is relatively low but now that portable colour sets are becoming more popular the possibility of running the battery flat increases.

The 1MΩ preset controls the point at which the LED glows.

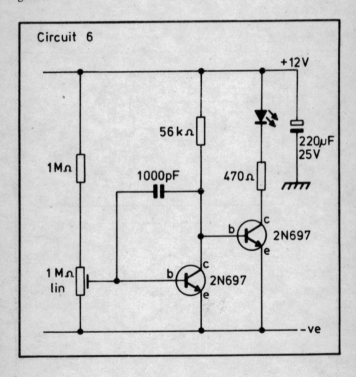

Circuit 6

CIRCUIT 7
Car Voltage Probe

This is a very simple circuit for testing points in the car electrical system. The circuit refers to a car which has the negative lead of the battery connected to chassis. The circuit is connected to the electrical system as shown and the probe is applied to the various test points.

When the probe is not touching any point on the system i.e. unconnected LED1 and LED2 will glow.

If the test probe touches a point near chassis potential LED1 will glow, LED2 extinguished.

If the test probe touches a point near the +12 volt battery potential LED2 glows, LED1 is extinguished.

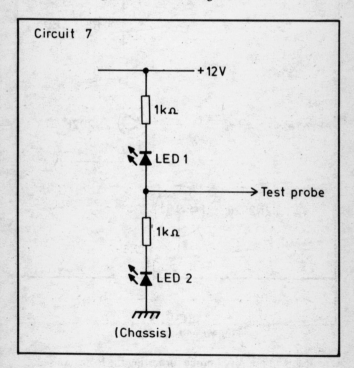

Circuit 7

+12V

1kΩ

LED 1

→ Test probe

1kΩ

LED 2

(Chassis)

CIRCUIT 8
Logic Level "1" Detector

This probe obtains its power from the 5 volt I C supply.

When the probe touches a point at logic level 1 the LED will glow. The transistor 2N2926 is a general purpose N P N silicon type which is readily available at very low cost. A transistor such as the BC107, BC108, BC109, BC147, BC148, BC149 or similar is also suitable.

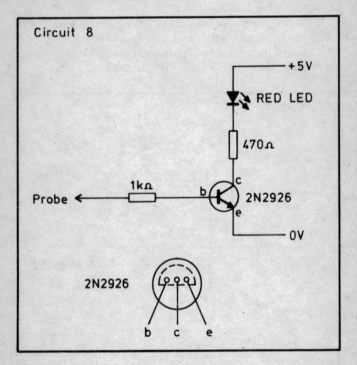

CIRCUIT 9
Improved Logic Probe

Circuit 9 is an improved probe for testing the logic levels in T T L circuits (T T L = Transistor Transistor Logic). The

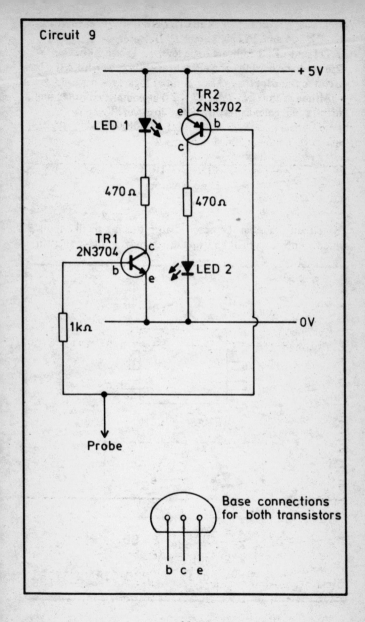

Circuit 9

LED 1

TR2
2N3702
e   b
   c

470 Ω

470 Ω

TR1
2N3704
   c
b
   e

LED 2

1 kΩ

+ 5V

0V

Probe

Base connections
for both transistors

b c e

11

circuit uses a pair of N P N and P N P transistors in this case the 2N3704 and 2N3702.

Tr1 and LED1 indicate logic level 1. Tr2 and LED2 indicate logic level 0. The circuit takes its power from the logic circuit 5 volt supply.

Although the 2N3704/2N3702 pair is specified other similar N P N/P N P pairs can be used e.g.   BC107/BC177
BC108/BC178

CIRCUIT 10
Opto Isolator

This circuit describes the opto isolator, this is a small circuit which combines a light emitting diode and a photo transistor

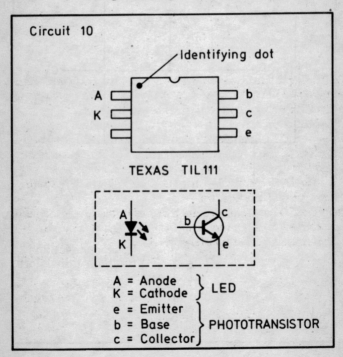

inside a light tight enclosure.

The circuit shown is the TEXAS TIL 111 opto isolator.

There is no electrical connection between input the light emitting diode and the output the photo transistor. The opto isolator will work at very high frequencies and can, for example, easily be used to provide an audio output to an external high fidelity amplifier from a non isolated chassis television set.

No details can be given as the circuit required would depend on the set in use.

Such a system should only be built by an experienced constructor with a knowledge of television circuits. **This is NOT a suitable project for the beginner.**

The opto isolator can also enable logic circuits to switch on mains equipment using SCRs or TRIACs, the opto isolator couples the circuits but they are completely separate electrically. It can also be used as a "noiseless" volume control.

CIRCUIT 11
Low Voltage Stabiliser

This simple circuit was used to supply 1½ volts at up to 125mA. A Green LED stabilises at 2.2 volts the voltage drop across the 2N697 gives an output voltage of about 1½ volts.

The circuit was used to supply equipment which originally ran on a U2 1½ volt cell. The stabiliser functions on a 6 volt D C input, this could be obtained from a 6.3 volt transformer and a bridge rectifier using four 1N4001 rectifiers.

The 2N697 is fitted with a TO5 heat sink which fits onto the transistor like a crown.

The TO5 heat sink is quite tricky to fit the first time you try it, the heat sink is a very tight fit (it is designed to be, so that maximum heat transfer takes place).

The stabiliser is a very simple one and it is not short circuit proof.

As a check a Red LED can be connected across the output, the Red LED will not glow unless the voltage is 1.6 volts or above, the output should be about 1.5 volts and the Red LED should be off.

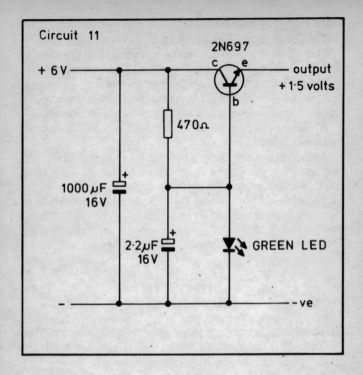

Circuit 11

+ 6 V

2N697

c   e

output
+ 1·5 volts

b

470Ω

1000μF
16 V

2·2μF
16 V

GREEN LED

−

− ve

CIRCUIT 12
Numbers Toy

This is a circuit that could from the basis of a simple
educational toy for use in say an infants school.

It consists of a 707 Common Anode display, seven SPST
switches and a 3 volt battery.

Certain positions and combinations of switches form the
numbers 0—9.

Two or three of these units could be combined in the same
box or case to show numbers up to 99 or 999.

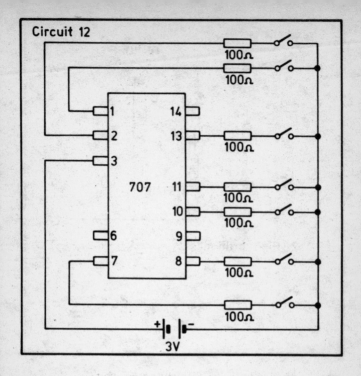

Circuit 12

CIRCUIT 13
SCR Tester

This is a simple circuit to test SCRs.

The circuit uses two LEDs one is a normal Red LED, the other is a high brilliance LED.

The maximum current rating of a standard LED is about 20mA. The maximum current rating of a high brilliance type can withstand a much higher current.

But what is an SCR?

An SCR is a Silicon Controlled Rectifier. Like a silicon rectifier it has an anode A and a cathode K plus a control electrode G the gate. The operation of an SCR, sometimes called a Thyristor — is that it is normally *non-conducting* when forward biased (unlike a normal rectifier) until a small

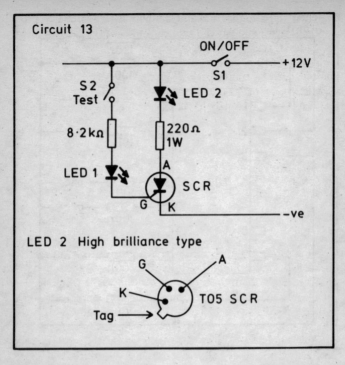

Circuit 13

ON/OFF
+12V
S1

S2
Test

LED 2

8·2kΩ

220Ω
1W

LED 1

A

SCR

G   K

−ve

LED 2 High brilliance type

G   A

K

Tag →   TO5 SCR

current is applied to the gate which triggers the SCR into
conduction. Once the SCR has switched to the conducting
state it continues to conduct until power is removed, it then
switches back to the non-conducting state. The gate can only
turn the SCR on, removal of power is required to switch the
SCR off again. The SCR can only control current flowing
in one direction, the TRIAC is a combination of two
SCRs connected so that they control the flow of current either
way i.e. the TRIAC can control AC, the SCR is only suitable
for unidirectional currents. To test, switch on and the SCR if
functional is in a non-conducting state, no current flows
through the SCR although it is forward biased (Anode positive)
so LED2 does not glow.

Operate test switch S2, a small gate current flows, the SCR
switches to conduction LED2 glows. Now switch off S2
removing the gate current, if LED2 still glows the SCR has

"latched" into conduction and is functional. Switching off S2 confirms that removing the gate current has no effect on the SCR once it is conducting.

The circuit was devised for testing TO5 size SCR's (these look like 2N697 transistors). Note that the TO5 metal casing may be connected to one of the leads i.e. casing not isolated.

The TO5 SCR usually has a maximum one amp current rating.

Note that the TO5 is not a device number it refers to the size or casing of the device — TO5 stands for Transistor Outline Number 5.

CIRCUIT 14
NPN Transistor Tester

This is a simple tester for small NPN transistors. Several testers for various semiconductor devices are described in this book but this is possibly the most useful one. It shows if a transistor is functional and also identifies the base lead. Transistors are sometimes sold as e.g. BC109s when they are really BC109 equivalents, absolutely genuine BC109 transistors are manufactured in the form TO18 with tiny metal cans having the leads arranged in a triangle emitter, base, collector, BC109 equivalents may be in an epoxy case with leads arranged base, collector, emitter.

The transistor gives one clue by identifying the base.

The tester uses a 3 pole 4 way switch 2 poles (2 sets) of contacts are not used. The 4 positions of the switch are OFF and 1, 2, 3 as indicated on the diagram.

The transistor under test has its three leads connected to the three leads from the switch as shown in the circuit diagram. The switch connects the positive pole of the battery to the three leads in turn, if the transistor is functional in one position of the switch 1, 2 or 3 all three Red LEDs will glow as a result of the transistor conducting. In the other two positions only the LED connected to the switch selector will glow.

When all 3 LEDs are glowing the transistor lead which is connected to the positive lead of the 9v battery, is the base, e.g. if the switch selector is at position 3 and all three LEDs are glowing the lead connected to 3 is the base of the transistor.

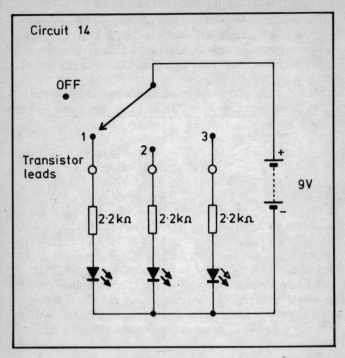

Circuit 14

OFF

1 2 3

Transistor leads

2·2kΩ 2·2kΩ 2·2kΩ

+ 9V −

CIRCUIT 15
1½ Volt Cell Tester

This is a circuit for testing 1½ volt cells as used in torches, radios etc.

A Red LED will not glow if connected to a 1½ volt cell as it requires about 1.6 volts to begin conduction. This circuit uses a 47 μF 6 volt electrolytic (a 12 volt or 16 volt type will also work) a DPDT slide switch and a Red LED connected as shown in Circuit 15.

What the circuit does is in effect to double the voltage. The 1½ volt cell under test is applied to the circuit with the

DPDT switch in the position as shown below. The switch is moved to the other position and if the cell is in reasonable condition the LED will flash once.

When the cell is connected the 47 μF electrolytic charges up to 1½ volts. When the DPDT switch is operated the electrolytic is connected in series with the 1½ volt cell so that the voltage across the LED is 1½ + 1½ = 3 volts, the LED conducts and discharges the capacitor the brief current flow produces the flash of light. The flash of light is very brief but easily visible.

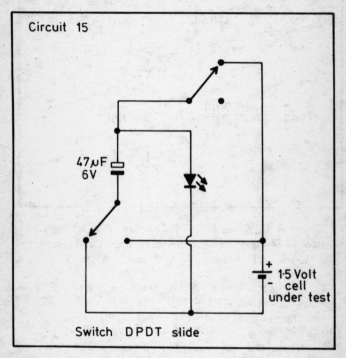

Circuit 15

47μF
6V

+
1·5 Volt
- cell
under test

Switch DPDT slide

CIRCUIT 16
Numeral "1" Display

In counters and clocks the first digit which is displayed may be only a "1" or blank.

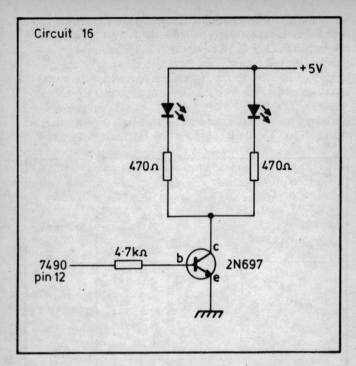

Circuit 16

The other digits may use a 7447 display driver IC and a 7 segment LED display because they are required to display 0 to 9 but a 7447 and a 7 segment display just to display 1 is expensive.

The 7447's take a BCD (Binary Coded Decimal) output from counters such as the 7490.

This circuit uses the output from pin 12 of a 7490 as a "1" or "Blank" display system.

The transistor drives two Red LEDs which can be positioned behind a piece of black card with two slots cut in it the same size and style as segments on a 7 segment display to give an effective "1".

The circuit takes its power from the 7490 and 7447 5 volt supply.

When pin 12 is at logic level 1 the LEDs will glow.

The circuit is designed for use with a 7490 or similar which is at the end of a divider chain. The 7490 does not count higher than 1 the next pulse resets the 7490 to 0. This would be the case with a clock with 12 hours display the tens of hours is either 1 or 0 only.

CIRCUIT 17
Matching LEDs for Brilliance

There are some circuits e.g. 2 LED FM tuning aid which require that LEDs should be closely matched in brilliance i.e., LEDs having the same current flowing through them should produce equal amounts of light. The simple circuit shown enables a pair to be selected from several LEDs.

The LEDs are connected in series so the current is the same through both of them.

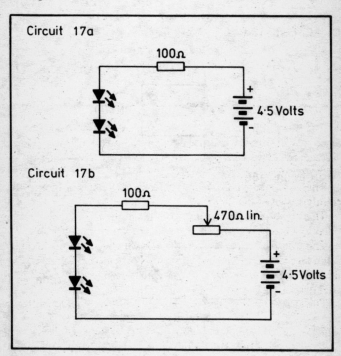

The current can be from a 4½ volt battery.

The circuit tests the LEDs at one current only. Circuit 17b shows a better test circuit the diode current can be varied.

A 470Ω Linear variable resistor can be used as shown.

CIRCUIT 18
Using LEDs on AC

LEDs can be used on AC supplies but the reverse breakdown voltage of a LED is very low. If the LED is used on AC e.g. as an indicator, a rectifier such as the 1N4001 can be connected as shown, this limits the reverse voltage to about 0.7 volts. See Circuit 18a.

Where two LEDs are connected in inverse parallel in circuits where the voltage is reversed to turn on the LEDs according to

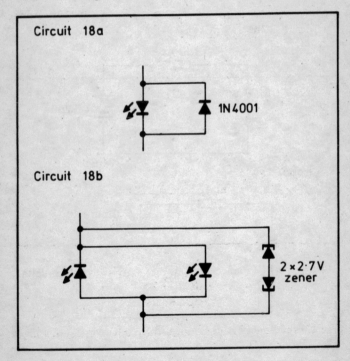

Circuit 18a

1N4001

Circuit 18b

2 × 2·7V zener

the polarity and the voltage exceeds 3 volts, two 2.7v 400mW zener diodes can be connected as shown, the zener diodes limit the voltage to about 3.4 volts in either direction. See Circuit 18b. These protection rectifiers and zener diodes are in addition to the normal series current limiting resistors.

CIRCUIT 19
The "2—LED" LED

There are now available two types of "twin" LED these consist of two LEDs in Inverse Parallel i.e. connected in parallel but the cathode of one LED is connected to the anode of the other and vice-versa.

The two types are a Red/Red pair and a Red/Green pair, which is the most interesting. Both the devices are in a single encapsulation which appears to be a single LED however, if the current flows in one direction it will glow Green, in the other direction it will glow Red.

The MV5491 is a Red/Green LED.

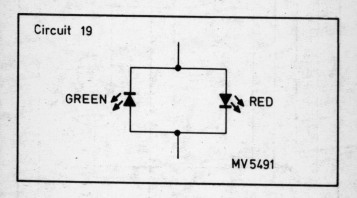

CIRCUIT 20
"Magic Boxes"

The "Magic Boxes" is an old idea which can be updated using the 2 colour LED.

There are two small boxes connected by *two* wires only.

One box is fitted with a switch the other with a light (the LED).

The switch is a 2 pole 3 way slide switch (or use a DPDT and a seperate ON/OFF switch).

The LED is OFF, the switch is operated the LED glows but then the switch is moved to the 3rd position the LED which was glowing Red, glows Green!

The trick works best with onlookers who have a slight knowledge of electricity but no knowledge of electronics.

Refer to the LED as a "subminiature light bulb" and ask your audience to try and explain how it works.

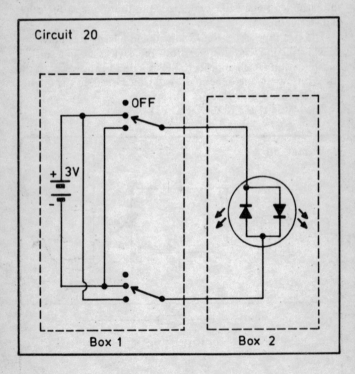

CIRCUIT 21
3-Colour LED

If a mains transformer with a 2 volt winding is available, this intriguing circuit can be built.

A transformer with a 1½ volt winding will probably work, the output at the low current required will be above 1½ volts. A four way rotary switch (2 pole 4 way, the second set of contacts not used) connects the 2 colour LED to DC of one polarity, DC of the opposite polarity, and AC, the 4th position is off. The LED will glow Red or Green but in the 3rd position AC both LEDs glow the Red and Green combined to give the impression of Yellow.

The LED is 3 colour, Red, Green and Yellow.

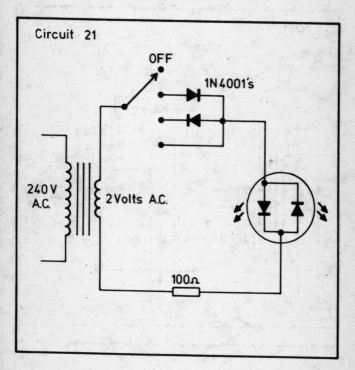

Circuit 21

OFF

1N4001's

240V A.C.

2 Volts A.C.

100Ω

CIRCUIT 22
2/3 Colour LED

This circuit is adapted from Circuit 21, a mains transformer with a 1½ volt or 2 volt secondary is an unusual item, but mains transformers with a 6 volt secondary are standard items.

The two 2.7v 400mW zener diodes protect the LEDs from reverse voltage without interfering with the circuit action.

This circuit was used with a 3 way slide switch for 2 colours only Red or Green but by using a 4 way switch the 3 colour effect as in Circuit 21 is easily obtained.

The circuit can be used with a 9 volt transformer if the limiting resistor is increased to 680Ω.

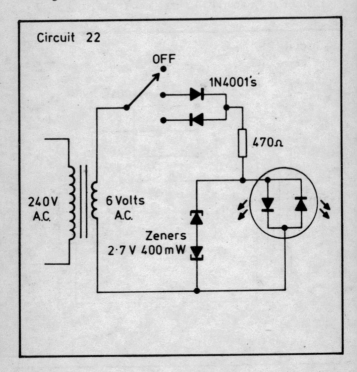

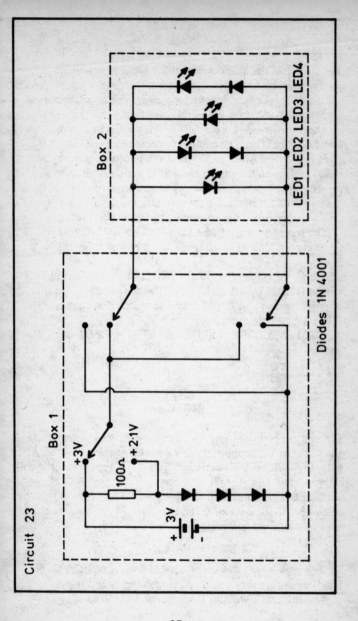

Circuit 23

Box 1

Box 2

LED1 LED2 LED3 LED4

Diodes 1N 4001

+3V

+2·1V

100Ω

3V

CIRCUIT 23
Super "Magic Boxes"

The circuit of the Magic Boxes in the simplest form uses the change of polarity to switch on two LEDs connected in "inverse parallel". This circuit shows how the idea can be extended by using a difference in voltage and reversal of polarity.

The rectifiers used are type 1N4001 all the LEDs are standard Red type. The circuit connected to the 3v battery gives two output voltages, 3 volts or 2.1 volts selected by a DPDT slide switch. The second DPDT slide switch changes polarity of the output so that 4 voltages are available 3 volts, 2.1 volts and 3 volts, 2.1 volts reversed polarity.

The magic boxes are connected by only *two* wires.

The secret is that a Red LED with a 1N4001 rectifier in series cannot glow at a voltage of 2.1 it requires the full 3 volts.

LED1, LED3 are Red LEDs, LED2, LED4 are Red LEDs with a 1N4001 in series. LED3, LED4 are connected in the opposite sense to LED1, LED2. The switch positions give the following combinations.

LED1 on, LED1 and LED2 on, LED3 on, LED3 and LED4 on.

CIRCUIT 24
AND Gate

Circuits can be built using LEDs and switches to demonstrate the principle of computer logic gates. Circuit 24 shows an AND gate, the switches are simple SPST ON/OFF types the LED will not glow unless A AND B are closed.

A LED on is equivalent to logic state "1" a LED off is equivalent to logic state "0" (zero).

The statement in Boolean Algebra would be:

$$A.B = 1$$

Although logic gates are associated with computers single logic devices are very common using switches and relays.

The automatic washing machine has built in logic e.g.

the tub will only fill with water if the machine is switched on
AND the door is closed (closing the door operates a micro-
switch). This safety feature is an AND gate. The gate shown is
the simplest A AND B, a "Two Input AND Gate". (If three
switches are used A, B, C it would be a 3 input AND gate, if four
a 4 input and so on. The equation for a 4 input AND gate
would be: A.B.C.D = 1).

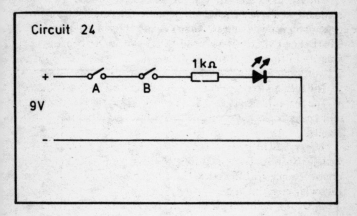

Circuit 24

CIRCUIT 25
NAND Gate

The gate in circuit 24 is an AND gate this is described as
positive logic A and B operated turn the LED on.

However practical computer logic circuits tend to use
negative logic, switches turning a circuit off.

Circuit 25 illustrates the function of a NOT AND gate or
NAND gate the circuit is a 2 input NAND gate A AND B
turn the LED off.

The logic IC type 7400 consists of four independent 2
input NAND gates and is known as a "QUAD 2 input NAND".
Circuit 25 is logically equivalent to a 2 input NAND gate as used
in the 7400.

7400 IC uses transistors to carry out the switching but this
circuit illustrates the idea.

For further details of 7400 ICs see book number BP58 "50 Circuits using 7400 series ICs" published by Bernard Babani (publishing) Ltd. The equation for a 2 input NAND gate is

$$\overline{A.B} = 1$$

the line or 'bar' indicates the negative function is a NOT AND gate.

A, B indicates switches closed therefore $\overline{A}$ indicates a switch open. So $\overline{A.B}$ indicates switches A and B open logic level 1. i.e. LED glowing.

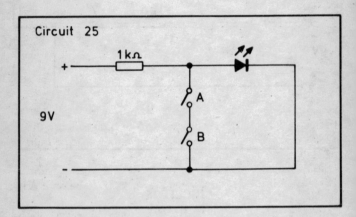

CIRCUIT 26
OR Gate

This describes another type of logic circuit the OR gate.

Switching on A OR B turns the LED on. This can be expressed in Boolean Algebra as

$$A + B = 1$$

This is a 2 input OR gate.

Using further switches a 3 or 4 input OR gate can be constructed.

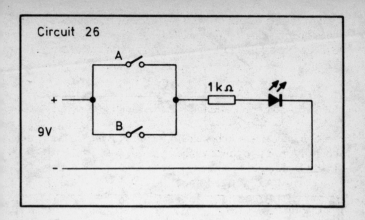

Circuit 26

CIRCUIT 27
Exclusive OR Gate

In Circuit 26, the OR gate, switching A or B on turns on the LED. This means that the LED will be on if A is on, B is on or both A and B are on.

However, there is another type of OR gate, known as the Exclusive OR or XOR that will allow the LED to be on if A is on, or B is on but not if both A and B are on.

With reference to Circuit 27, the switches A1 and A2 are ganged together as are the switches for B1 and B2. (Alternatively two DPDT slide switches could be used one for A and one for B).

The circuit is really a combination of an OR gate

$$A + B = 1$$

and a NAND gate

$$\overline{A.B} = 1$$

As the gates are connected together the two expressions can also be combined by the rules of Boolean Algebra to give:

$$A.\overline{B} + \overline{A}.B = 1$$

which is the equation for a XOR gate.

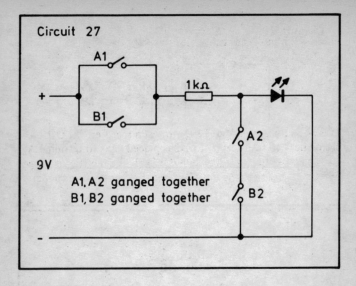

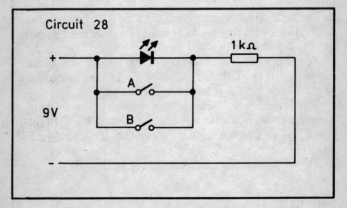

CIRCUIT 28
NOR Gate

The negative logic equivalent of Circuit 26 is used, this is the NOT OR gate or NOR gate. Either A or B turns the LED off. The function can be expressed

32

$$\overline{A + B} = 1$$

This is a 2 input NOR gate.

CIRCUIT 29
Rectifier Tester

This circuit uses two Red LEDs to test a rectifier. LED1 is placed next to terminal B, LED2 is placed next to terminal A.

The test switch is a SPST ON/OFF. If the rectifier is functional LED1 glows this indicates that the rectifier under

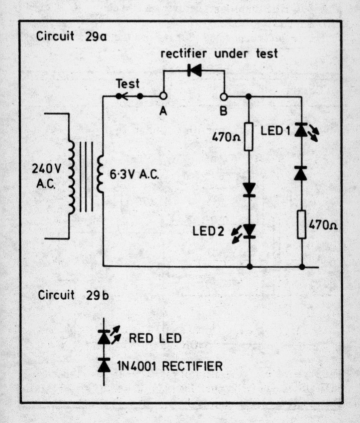

Circuit 29a

rectifier under test

Test

A   B

240V A.C.   6·3V A.C.   470Ω   LED1

LED2   470Ω

Circuit 29b

RED LED

1N4001 RECTIFIER

test has the cathode connected to point B. If LED2 glows it indicates that the cathode is at A.

If both LED1 and LED2 glow the rectifier is short circuit and useless. The 1N4001 rectifiers in series with the LEDs protect the LEDs from the reverse voltage.

The transformer is a 6v, 100mA type intended for powering transistor circuits.

CIRCUIT 30
Simple Rectifier Test

This is an ultra simple rectifier test. A two colour Red/Green LED is used as the indicator.

The circuit is connected so that when the rectifier under test

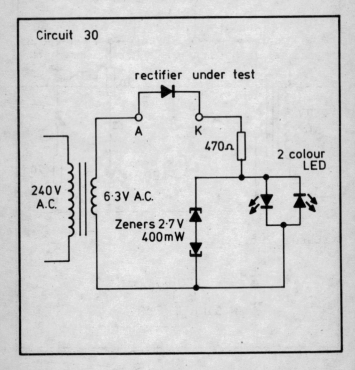

is connected as shown the Red LED glows (try the circuit with a 1N4001 rectifier).

The two terminals can then be marked A (anode) and K (cathode).

The two zener diodes (2.7 volt 400mW type) protect the LED from damage due to excessive reverse voltage. If the rectifier under test is short circuit both the Red and Green LEDs will glow together and the LED will appear Yellow.

CIRCUIT 31
Simple Changeover Circuit

This circuit uses a simple SPST ON/OFF switch to change from LED1 to LED2.

The circuit depends on the property of the voltage drop across a LED being very constant.

LED1 and LED$_2$ are in parallel but LED1 has a 1N4001 rectifier in series which produces a further voltage drop across the combination. With the switch on, LED2 clamps the voltage

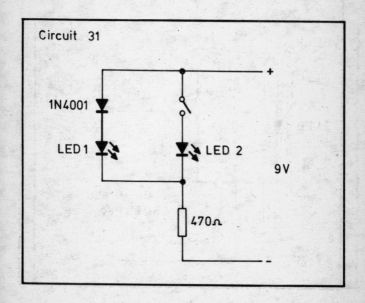

Circuit 31

1N4001

LED 1

LED 2

9 V

470Ω

at about 1.6 volts, LED1 cannot glow. With the switch in the off position the current can flow via LED1 and it glows.

> Switch closed LED2 lights
>
> Switch open LED1 lights.

CIRCUIT 32
2—Colour Changeover Circuit

This circuit again uses a single ON/OFF switch to changeover from one LED to another.

In this case a Red and a Green LED are used. The forward voltage of a Green LED is higher than a Red LED with the switch closed the Red and Green are in parallel and the Red LED glows. With the switch open the current can flow through the Green LED and it glows.

> Switch closed LED2 glows
>
> Switch open LED1 glows.

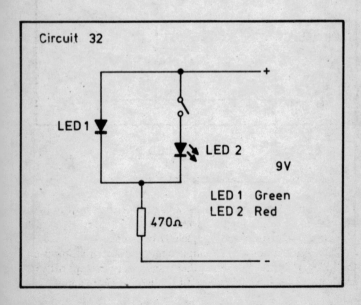

Circuit 32

LED 1

LED 2

9V

LED 1   Green
LED 2   Red

470Ω

CIRCUIT 33
ZN414 IC Supply

The popular Ferranti ZN414 TRF radio IC requires a supply of about 1½ volts.

This simple regulated supply is ideal for use in a portable radio using a ZN414 with a 9 volt audio amplifier.

The voltage is stabilised by the LED at about 1.6 volts for stability the OA91 produces a slight voltage drop to below 1.6, as sometimes the ZN414 may be unstable if operated at 1.6v.

The LED is a Red type.

The OA91 is a germanium point contact diode any similar diode is suitable OA90, OA81 etc.

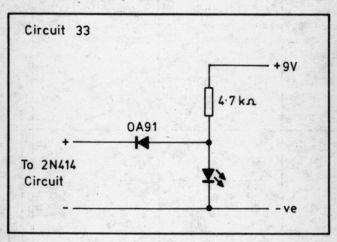

CIRCUIT 34
Simple "Snap" Indicator

This is a simple indicator to show who pressed their button first. Two Green LEDs are used to give indication.

The two transistors are type 2N697 or similar.

The circuit action is very simple operating switch S1 turns on the LED1 and this causes the other transistor to be kept off so LED2 cannot light. Similarly if LED2 lights, LED1 cannot.

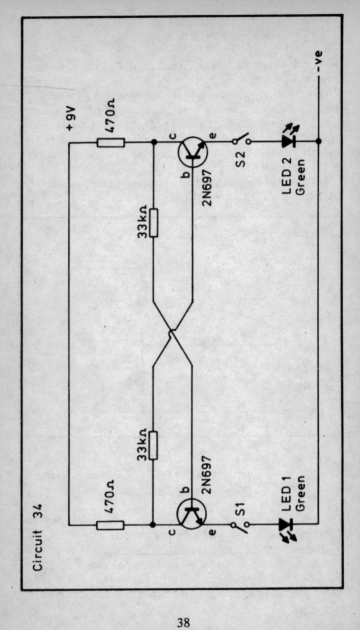

Circuit 34

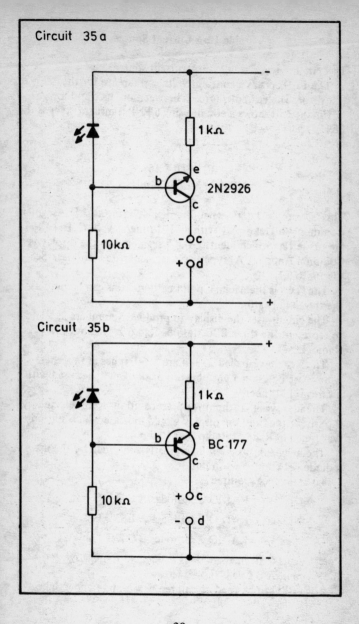

Circuit 35a

1 kΩ

b — e — 2N2926
c

− o c
+ o d

Circuit 35b

1 kΩ

b — e — BC 177
c

+ o c
− o d

10 kΩ

39

CIRCUIT 35
Stable 1mA Current Source

This circuit gives a stable 1mA current source.

The LED acts as a constant voltage reference for the 2N2926 transistor. The current source is between points c and d.

Circuit 35b shows a circuit using a PNP transistor such as the BC177.

CIRCUIT 36
Simple 3 Digit Display

This is a simple 3 digit capability display using a LED 7 segment Common Anode display with an FM tuner. A, B, C, D, E, F, G are the letters which identify the 7 segments, as the display is a Common Anode (CA) type the 7 segments are cathodes. See Circuit 36a.

The (DP) is the decimal point cathode, this can be used as the stereo indicator.

The circuit uses the display to produce 3 numbers 2, 3 and 4 to represent the three BBC stations Radio 2, Radio 3 and Radio 4.

The switches labelled 2, 3, 4 are SPST types in fact these were spare poles on a push button bank of switches used with a varicap FM tuner.

The idea was that the three preset stations were selected by 3 push buttons and the display would indicate which station was tuned in Radio 2 Radio 3 or Radio 4.

The mechanical switching is greatly simplified by the use of a diode network. See Circuit 36b.

The sequence required is

RADIO 2 cathodes A B D E G "on"

RADIO 3 cathodes A B C D G "on"

RADIO 4 cathodes B C F G "on"

"on" means that the cathode is connected to negative and the segment A B C D E F or G glows.

The (DP) can be used as a stereo beacon by connecting

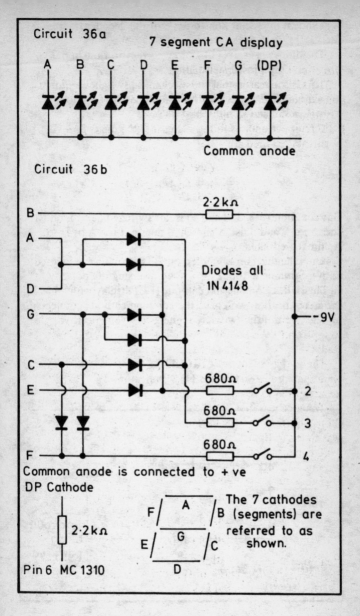

Circuit 36a

7 segment CA display

A   B   C   D   E   F   G   (DP)

Common anode

Circuit 36b

B ——— 2·2kΩ ———

A

D

G   Diodes all
                     1N 4148

C   —9V

E ——— 680Ω ———o o——— 2

——— 680Ω ———o o——— 3

F ——— 680Ω ———o o——— 4

Common anode is connected to +ve
DP Cathode

2·2kΩ

Pin 6 MC 1310

The 7 cathodes
(segments) are
referred to as
shown.

41

it as shown in Circuit 36b to pin 6 of the decoder (if it is MC1310 type).

The diodes type 1N4148 allow current to flow in one direction only providing isolation.

This is the reason that the mechanical switches required are simple SPST types the 1N4148 diodes are functioning as switches. See Circuit 36b.

Circuit action is as follows, consider the digits 2, 3, 4. Segments required are

$$
\begin{array}{llllllll}
2 & A & B & . & D & E & . & G \\
3 & A & B & C & D & . & . & G \\
4 & . & B & C & . & . & F & G \\
\end{array}
$$

B is common to 2, 3, 4 and so is not switched i.e. it is on all the time. 2 and 3 use A and D. 4 does not use A or D so A and D are linked.

Thus the diagram is worked out. The circuit can be used with a common cathode display by reversing the polarity of all the diodes. A common cathode (CC) display which has 7 anode connections will have the common cathode connected to negative and the switches connect to 9 volts positive.

CIRCUIT 37
Current Flow Indicator

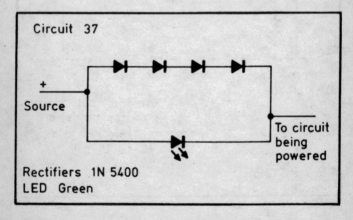

Circuit 37

+
Source

To circuit being powered

Rectifiers 1N 5400
LED Green

This simple circuit indicates that current is flowing, for example in a battery charger circuit.

The maximum current through the rectifiers should be 3 amps. The rectifiers are type 1N5400. The LED is a Green type. Note that the circuit produces a constant voltage drop of about 3 volts.

No series resistor is required for the LED as the rectifiers shunt away nearly all the current.

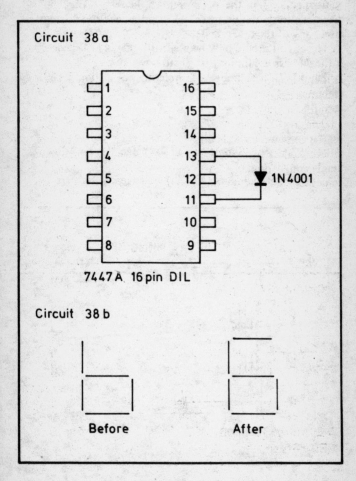

Circuit 38 a

7447 A 16 pin DIL

Circuit 38 b

Before   After

CIRCUIT 38
Improved "6" Display for CA 7-Segment Display

Common Anode (CA) 7 segment LED displays can be driven by a 7447A IC decoder/driver. The digit 6 produced is a "tail-less six" by connecting a 1N4001 between pins 13 and 11 of the 7447A, a tail can be added as shown.

The diagram shows the connection, the original wiring, components etc. of the 7447A remain the same. The diagram also shows the two sixes. This connection does not affect any of the other digits.

The circuit should only be used with the 7447A device. If the 7447 is used it may be slightly over run.

The 7447A is an improved 'more rugged' version of the 7447.

CIRCUIT 39
Simple Ni-Cad Recharger

AA size Nickel Cadmium (Ni-Cad) rechargeable cells are

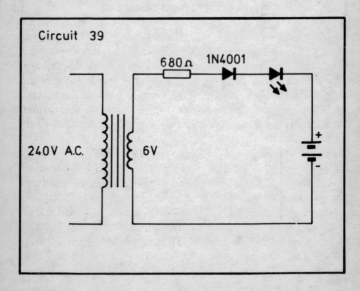

Circuit 39

readily available (the AA size is exactly equivalent to U7, HP7 etc.)

This circuit is a simple charger. The mains transformer can be a 6 volt 100mA type.

The 680Ω resistor limits the charging current, the cells should not be left on charge for more than 12 hours. The circuit was used to recharge two AA cells.

The LED indicates that a charging current is flowing.

CIRCUIT 40
555 LED Flasher

This uses the 555 timer circuit, now a standard IC available at low cost, to flash two Red LEDs. The 555 is in an 8 pin DIL package.

The 4.7μF capacitor is part of the timing circuit and determines the flashing rate.

CIRCUIT 41
Flashing Seconds Display

Digital clocks can be built using 7400 series ICs and 7 segment displays. For economy a 4 digit hours and minutes display is used but at the cost of 1 resistor a flashing seconds display can be obtained. The CA displays have decimal points not used in a clock display, by connecting the decimal point of the tens of minutes display to the output from the second 7490 divider a flashing display is obtained. The display is quite dim but easily visible because it flashes.

The DP cathode of a CA display is usually pin 6.

The circuit 41a shows a typical clock circuit 7490 ICs are connected as ÷ 5, ÷ 10, ÷ 10 and ÷ 6 circuits the output from pin 11 of the second 7490 is one pulse per second. This is for 50Hz mains, on 60Hz mains the 7490's would be ÷ 6, ÷10, ÷ 10, ÷ 6 however the output from pin 11 of the 2nd 7490 will again be one pulse per second. The practical circuit is shown in circuit 41b.

In a similar way the DP cathode of the tens of hours digit

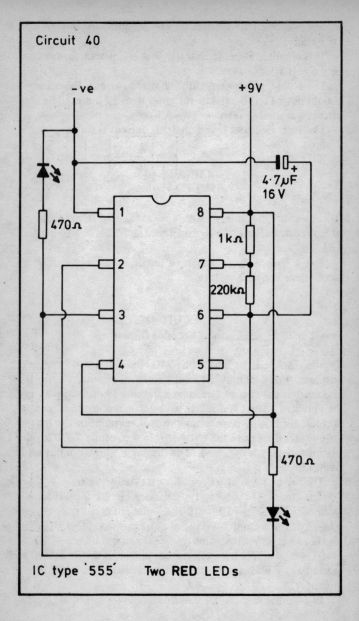

Circuit 40

−ve   +9V

4·7μF
16 V

470Ω

1   8

1kΩ

2   7

220kΩ

3   6

4   5

470Ω

IC type '555'   Two RED LEDs

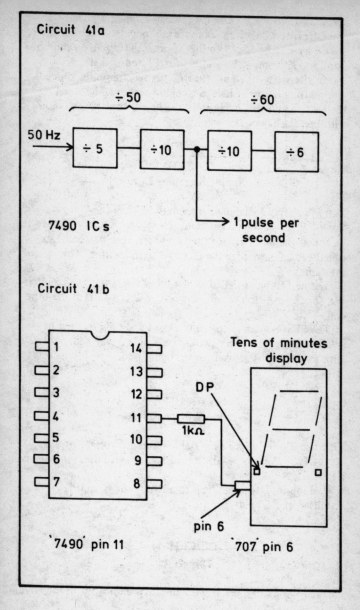

Circuit 41a

÷50 : 50 Hz → ÷5 → ÷10 → • → ÷10 → ÷6   ÷60

7490 ICs

→ 1 pulse per second

Circuit 41b

Tens of minutes display

DP

1kΩ

pin 6

'7490' pin 11   '707' pin 6

47

display could be used as a PM indicator, when a 12 hour display is used, this is much more complicated since a ÷ 2 circuit would have to be added to the clock so that the DP would be "on" for 12 hours (PM) and off for 12 hours (AM).

An alternative is to use the one per second pulses to feed circuit 16 and use 2 LEDs as a colon positioned between the tens of minutes display and the hours display, the colon will then flash once per second.

CIRCUIT 42
Simple Signalling Device

This is a simple signalling device derived from the "Magic Boxes" idea. A person can send two signals Red or Green to the person at the other end of the two wires. The person being called can acknowledge the message "Red" with a "Green" to the caller.

The person being called with a "Red" puts the SPST switch in the "open" position which puts on the Green LED at the other end.

The SPST switch is normally closed and only opened to acknowledge. The other switch is a 2 pole 3 way slide switch with position OFF, signal Green, signal Red.

CIRCUIT 43
Precision Voltage Reference

This circuit produces a very stable reference voltage of 1.60 volts. Two Texas type TIL209 LEDs are used, the transistor is a BC177 PNP silicon type.

The input voltage can be 6 to 12 volts the output is stabilised at 1.60 volts.

CIRCUIT 44
Fuse Tester

This is a simple fuse tester with a positive indication if the Green

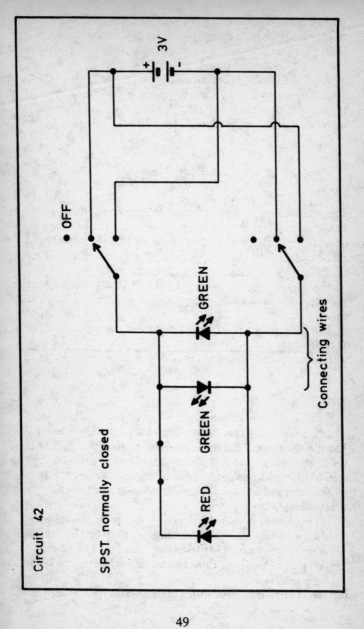

Circuit 42

3V

OFF

SPST normally closed

GREEN

GREEN

RED

Connecting wires

49

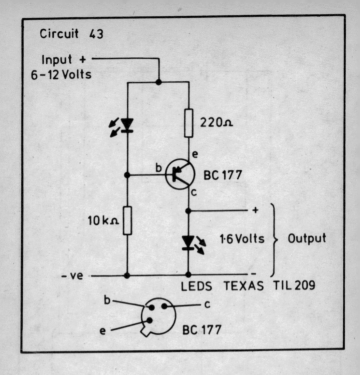

Circuit 43

Input +
6 – 12 Volts

220 Ω

e
b   BC 177
c

10 kΩ

1·6 Volts } Output

– ve

+

–

LEDS TEXAS TIL 209

b   c

e   BC 177

LED glows fuse is O.K. if the Red LED glows fuse is blown. In fact the Green LED indicates a short circuit, the Red LED indicates an open circuit.

A short circuit is produced by an intact fuse (very low resistance) and the open circuit by a blown fuse (infinite resistance).

If holders to suit several sizes of fuses can be obtained and connected as shown, many different fuses can be tested easily. It is particularly useful for testing the fuses used in 13 amp mains plugs, these have a ceramic body and it is impossible to see the fuse wire.

The switch is a push button press to test type.

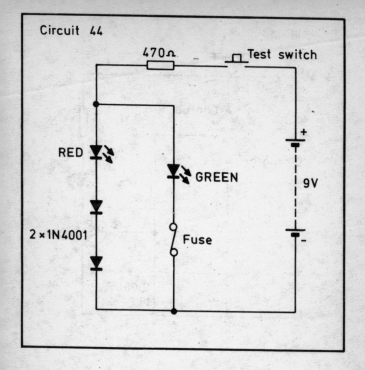

Circuit 44

470Ω Test switch

RED

GREEN

2 × 1N4001

Fuse

9V
+
−

CIRCUIT 45
Simple Timer

This simple timer uses an LED as time elapsed indicator. The
LED can be set so that it is ON but goes OFF after a certain
time or OFF but comes ON after a certain time.

The time elapsed is controlled by the charging or discharging
of C1 an electrolytic capacitor, the value shown is 100 μF but
this can be altered to change the timing period.

The charge/discharge switch is a DPDT slide switch
connected as SPDT switch.

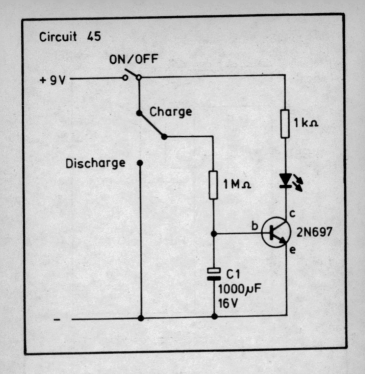

Circuit 45

CIRCUIT 46
Fluorescent Indicator Device Filament Tester

As the LED 7 segment digital display is now used in current
equipment the earlier fluorescent display devices are
obosolescent and available at low cost as surplus. The device
is as shown in Circuit 46a. The fluorescent indicator is a
thermionic device, it has a filament which emits electrons when
heated, a control grid and 7 anodes which form the segments
(plus an extra one for a decimal point). The anodes glow
green or pale blue when they are at 18 volts positive and the
control grid is also positive.

The simple Circuit 46b shows how to test the filaments
which are rated at about 0.7v to 1½ volts depending on the

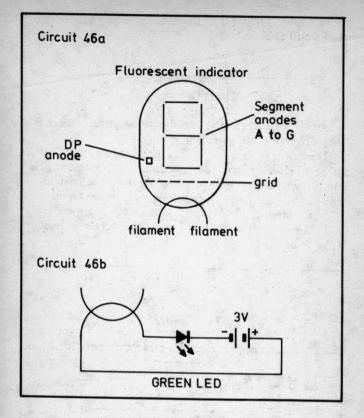

Circuit 46a

Fluorescent indicator

Segment anodes A to G

DP anode

grid

filament   filament

Circuit 46b

3V

GREEN LED

device.

The Green LED with a 3v battery provides a simple test when connected in series with the filament, if the LED glows the filament is intact.

The devices are wire ended and the wires will be control grid, anodes A, B, C, D, E, F, G and DP, and two filament connections. The filament wires are sometimes covered in Red sleeving which helps to identify them.

The devices are quite fragile they are vacuum tubes if the glass has cracked and air has entered they are useless.

Note that many of the clock radios sold although described as "LED display" are in fact fitted with fluorescent displays.

If the display is Red it is a LED, if Green or pale Blue it is a fluorescent type.

CIRCUIT 47
Magnet Operated LED

Tiny reed switches are now available at low prices and this is a simple circuit to illustrate their use.

The switch consists of two iron reeds sealed in a small glass tube. The reeds overlap but do not touch, in a magnetic field they become magnetised and spring together. The reeds are gold plated so that a good contact of low resistance is made. When the magnetic field is removed the reeds spring apart.

In Circuit 47 bringing a small magnet near the reed switch will turn on the LED.

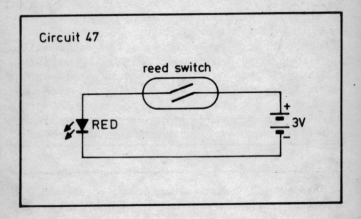

CIRCUIT 48
Variable Capacitor Tester

Variable capacitors are one of the more expensive components that the hobbyist may have to buy so it is very worthwhile making use of surplus items or those removed from old broken radios.

The most common fault with a variable capacitor is a short circuit at some point, the rotors and stators may touch or there may be particles of metal or dust in between the moving vanes.

If you are drilling an aluminium chassis or a printed circuit make sure that tiny flashes of aluminium or copper do not find their way into the variable capacitor you were intending to use.

The rotors are the moving vanes. The stators are the fixed plates. The variable capacitor should have infinite resistance to DC between the stators and rotors at all points.

The variable capacitor is connected into the Circuit 48 as shown. The spindle is rotated slowly several times. This should be done in a darkened room. In a test a 2.2 MΩ resistor in series with a LED and a 9v battery gave a tiny but still just visible gleam in a dark room so that the LED can detect even a leakage as small as 2.2 MΩ.

Take care using the circuit that you do not hold the capacitor in one hand touching the stators and rotate it with the other hand touching the rotors the LED might just glow because a tiny current is passing through you!

If possible fit a plastic knob on the tuning spindle so that the rotors are insulated from your fingers. The LED should not glow at any point on the capacitors travel. If it does, there is a short circuit perhaps one of the rotors is slightly bent and just touches the stators, it must be very carefully bent away, a tiny repositioning may be all that is necessary. A small paint brush is useful for removing any dust or metallic particles stuck in between the vanes.

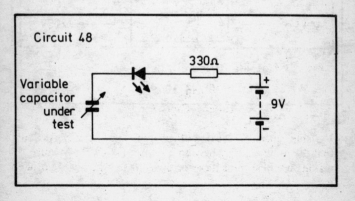

Circuit 48

Variable capacitor under test

330Ω

9V

CIRCUIT 49
LM3909 Flasher

This is a circuit which uses a small IC specially developed for use with LEDs.

Using the very simple Circuit 49 with a single 1½ volt cell gives a low current flashing display.

The current drawn is less than 0.5mA. Special "flashing" Red LEDs are now available but they (at the time of writing) are very expensive in comparison to an ordinary Red LED

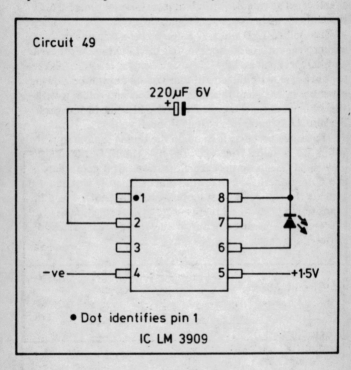

CIRCUIT 50
LED "Line of Light"

This circuit uses 4 LEDs which light in sequence as the applied voltage increases, the idea can be extended to use 5 or 6 LEDs, it can be used as a crude voltmeter if miniature preset variable resistors were used to give a 1 volt increment between the LEDs.

The circuit functions as a voltage divider the LED with the highest value resistor in parallel will glow first. In the circuit 50 as shown the LEDs will glow in sequence LED1., LED2, LED3, LED4 as the voltage increases.

The 'line of light' will take a heavy current if used as a voltmeter.

LED1 will glow when the voltage drops across the 1.2kΩ resistor is 1.6 volts all the LEDs LED1–LED4 will be glowing when the voltage drop across the 680Ω resistor is 1.6 volts.

The maximum voltage applied should be just high enough the light LED4.

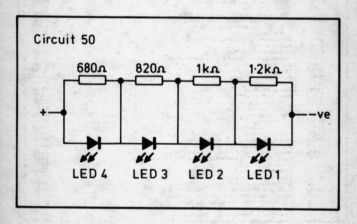

160	Coil Design and Construction Manual	£2.50
205	Hi-Fi Loudspeaker Enclosures	£2.95
208	Practical Stereo & Quadrophony Handbook	£0.75
214	Audio Enthusiast's Handbook	£0.85
219	Solid State Novelty Projects	£0.85
220	Build Your Own Solid State Hi-Fi and Audio Accessories	£0.85
222	Solid State Short Wave Receivers for Beginners	£2.95
225	A Practical Introduction to Digital ICs	£2.50
226	How to Build Advanced Short Wave Receivers	£2.95
227	Beginners Guide to Building Electronic Projects	£1.95
228	Essential Theory for the Electronics Hobbyist	£2.50
BP2	Handbook of Radio, TV, Industrial and Transmitting Tube and Valve Equivalents	£0.60
BP6	Engineer's & Machinist's Reference Tables	£1.25
BP7	Radio & Electronic Colour Codes Data Chart	£0.95
BP27	Chart of Radio, Electronic, Semiconductor and Logic Symbols	£0.95
BP28	Resistor Selection Handbook	£0.60
BP29	Major Solid State Audio Hi-Fi Construction Projects	£0.85
BP33	Electronic Calculator Users Handbook	£1.50
BP36	50 Circuits Using Germanium Silicon and Zener Diodes	£1.50
BP37	50 Projects Using Relays, SCRs and TRIACs	£2.95
BP39	50 (FET) Field Effect Transistor Projects	£2.95
BP42	50 Simple LED Circuits	£1.95
BP44	IC 555 Projects	£2.95
BP45	Projects in Opto-Electronics	£1.95
BP48	Electronic Projects for Beginners	£1.95
BP49	Popular Electronic Projects	£2.50
BP53	Practical Electronics Calculations and Formulae	£3.95
BP54	Your Electronic Calculator & Your Money	£1.35
BP56	Electronic Security Devices	£2.50
BP58	50 Circuits Using 7400 Series IC's	£2.50
BP62	The Simple Electronic Circuit & Components (Elements of Electronics — Book 1)	£3.50
BP63	Alternating Current Theory (Elements of Electronics — Book 2)	£3.50
BP64	Semiconductor Technology (Elements of Electronics — Book 3)	£3.50
BP66	Beginners Guide to Microprocessors and Computing	£1.95
BP68	Choosing and Using Your Hi-Fi	£1.65
BP69	Electronic Games	£1.75
BP70	Transistor Radio Fault-finding Chart	£0.95
BP72	A Microprocessor Primer	£1.75
BP74	Electronic Music Projects	£2.50
BP76	Power Supply Projects	£2.50
BP77	Microprocessing Systems and Circuits (Elements of Electronics — Book 4)	£2.95
BP78	Practical Computer Experiments	£1.75
BP80	Popular Electronic Circuits - Book 1	£2.95
BP84	Digital IC Projects	£1.95
BP85	International Transistor Equivalents Guide	£3.50
BP86	An Introduction to BASIC Programming Techniques	£1.95
BP87	50 Simple LED Circuits — Book 2	£1.35
BP88	How to Use Op-Amps	£2.95
BP89	Communication (Elements of Electronics — Book 5)	£2.95
BP90	Audio Projects	£2.50
BP91	An Introduction to Radio DXing	£1.95
BP92	Electronics Simplified — Crystal Set Construction	£1.75
BP93	Electronic Timer Projects	£1.95
BP94	Electronic Projects for Cars and Boats	£1.95
BP95	Model Railway Projects	£1.95
BP97	IC Projects for Beginners	£1.96
BP98	Popular Electronic Circuits — Book 2	£2.25
BP99	Mini-matrix Board Projects	£2.50
BP101	How to Identify Unmarked ICs	£0.95
BP103	Multi-circuit Board Projects	£1.95
BP104	Electronic Science Projects	£2.95
BP105	Aerial Projects	£1.95
BP106	Modern Op-amp Projects	£1.95
BP107	30 Solderless Breadboard Projects — Book 1	£2.25
BP108	International Diode Equivalents Guide	£2.25
BP109	The Art of Programming the 1K ZX81	£1.95
BP110	How to Get Your Electronic Projects Working	£2.50
BP111	Audio (Elements of Electronics — Book 6)	£3.50
BP112	A Z-80 Workshop Manual	£3.50
BP113	30 Solderless Breadboard Projects — Book 2	£2.25
BP114	The Art of Programming the 16K ZX81	£2.50
BP115	The Pre-computer Book	£1.95
BP117	Practical Electronic Building Blocks — Book 1	£1.95
BP118	Practical Electronic Building Blocks — Book 2	£1.95
BP119	The Art of Programming the ZX Spectrum	£2.50
BP120	Audio Amplifier Fault-finding Chart	£0.95
BP121	How to Design and Make Your Own PCB's	£2.50
BP122	Audio Amplifier Construction	£2.25
BP123	A Practical Introduction to Microprocessors	£2.50
BP124	Easy Add-on Projects for Spectrum, ZX81 & Ace	£2.75
BP125	25 Simple Amateur Band Aerials	£1.95
BP126	BASIC & PASCAL in Parallel	£1.50
BP127	How to Design Electronic Projects	£2.25
BP128	20 Programs for the ZX Spectrum and 16K ZX81	£1.95
BP129	An Introduction to Programming the ORIC-1	£1.95
BP130	Micro Interfacing Circuits — Book 1	£2.25
BP131	Micro Interfacing Circuits — Book 2	£2.75